ANIMAL HUSB

TONY HUSBA

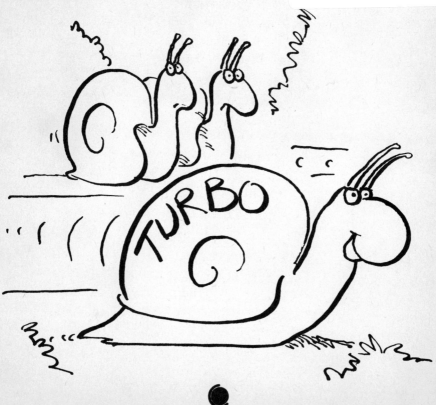

SPHERE

Sphere Books Limited

FOR PAUL WITH LOVE

Grateful thanks to *Punch*

First published in Great Britain by Sphere Books Ltd 1986
27 Wright's Lane, London W8 5SW
Copyright © 1986 by Tony Husband

Printed and bound in Finland by
Werner Söderström Osakeyhtiö

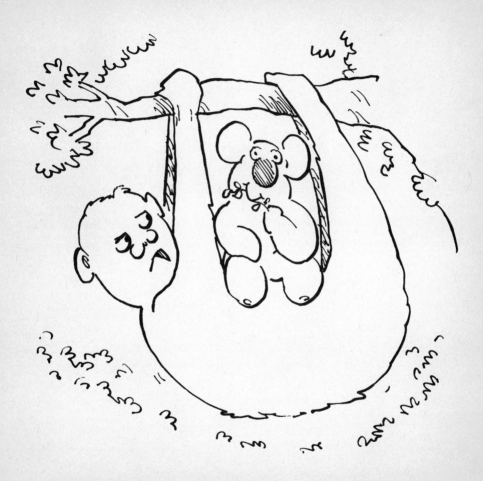

OI! SOD OFF

YOU'RE RIGHT, THEY ARE MOLE HILLS

**WE'RE FOLLOWING UP REPORTS OF
SHEEP RUSTLING – YOU'VE NOT SEEN
ANYTHING SUSPICIOUS HAVE YOU?**

DEAR MUM AND DAD, AT LAST I'M AMONGST FRIENDS . . .

AYE! DOWN THE LANE AND TURN LEFT AFTER
THE THIRD SQUASHED HEDGEHOG

DON'T SHOOT! HERE TAKE THEM!

LOOK NOAH, OVER THERE

**EXCUSE MY STARING, BUT I'VE NOT HAD LUNCH
WITH AN ANTEATER BEFORE**

THAT DOG'S COVERED IN FLEAS

**DON'T PANIC HE'S ONLY
SELLING ENCYCLOPAEDIAS**

LISTEN. ANY FRIEND OF NORMAN'S IS A FRIEND OF MINE

ENDANGERED SPECIES OR NOT, I DON'T LIKE THE
WAY IT JUST STROLLS IN AND LAYS ITS
DAMNED EGGS IN MY LIVING ROOM

IF YOU MUST KNOW, I CAN'T STAND PARROTS

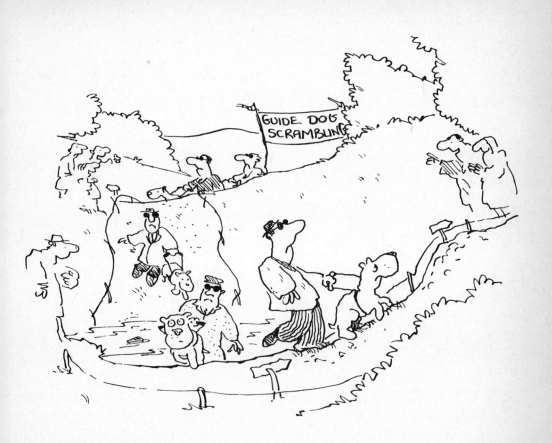

OK, BOY, WHERE'VE YOU BURIED GRANDAD?

WILDLIFE'S NOT WHAT IT USED TO BE, BOSWORTH

YOU'LL HAVE TO EXCUSE MY HUSBAND,
HE WAS REARED BY BABOONS

**SARGE: I THINK WE'VE SPOTTED THE
ESCAPED CIRCUS ELEPHANT. OVER**

**COULD YOU RING BACK, HE'S JUST TRYING
TO OUT STARE THE DOG**

THIS IS QUITE REMARKABLE. IT SEEMS THE FEMALE IS KNITTING ME A CARDIGAN

FIND ANOTHER SLUG, DEAR?

PSST! HARRY, WHAT'S IT LIKE?

I SEE TERENCE HAS GOT RELIGION

A PINT OF WHATEVER HIPPOPOTAMUS'S HAVE

MY GOD, LOOK AT THAT!

MY HUSBAND COLLECTS DOGENDS

YOU SPOIL THAT CAT, HENRY

**TCH! HAVE YOU ELECTRIFIED
THE BIRD BATH AGAIN?**

AND WHERE THE HELL HAVE YOU BEEN?

I WONDER WHAT IT SAID ON THE INVITATION?

THIS ONE NOT ONLY TALKS, HE DOES FEMALE IMPERSONATIONS

I WOULDN'T NORMALLY COME OUT
ON CHRISTMAS EVE, YOU KNOW

YOU'LL NOT GET AWAY WITH IT!

CHARLES, I HONESTLY DON'T THINK STAMPING ON IT
WILL DO MUCH GOOD

HANDS UP! THESE RABBITS HAVE BEEN
BUNGED UP FOR TWO MONTHS.
ONE FALSE MOVE AND YOU GET IT.

ADOPTED? MOM, DAD WHAT ARE YOU SAYING?

IT MAY BE QUICKER, TOMSON,
BUT IT'S UPSETTING THE VISITOR

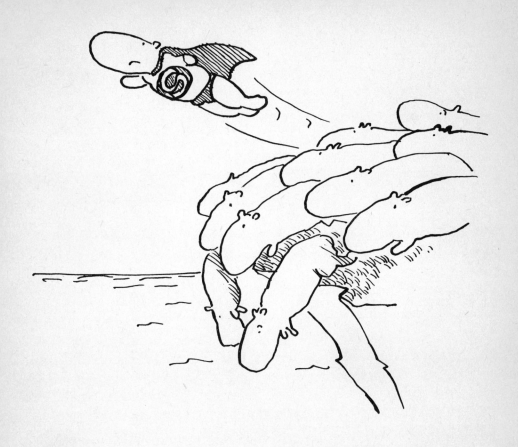